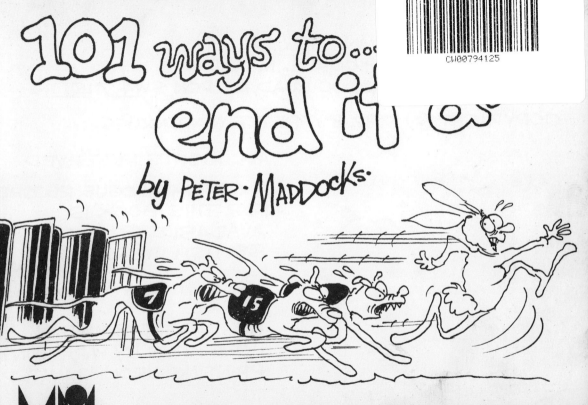

101 ways to... end it all

by PETER·MADDOCKS·

MICHAEL O'MARA BOOKS LIMITED

FIRST PUBLISHED IN 1992 BY
MICHAEL O'MARA BOOKS LIMITED
9, LION YARD, TREMADOC ROAD, LONDON SW4 7NQ.

COPYRIGHT © 1992 BY PETER MADDOCKS.

A CIP CATALOGUE RECORD
FOR THIS BOOK IS
AVAILABLE FROM THE
BRITISH LIBRARY.

ISBN 1-85479-166-4

PRINTED AND BOUND IN
HONG KONG BY PARAMOUNT
PRINTING GROUP LIMITED.

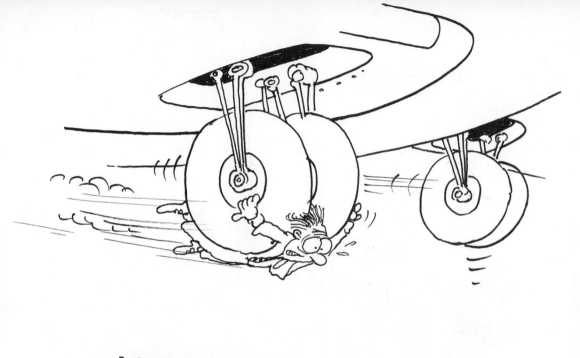

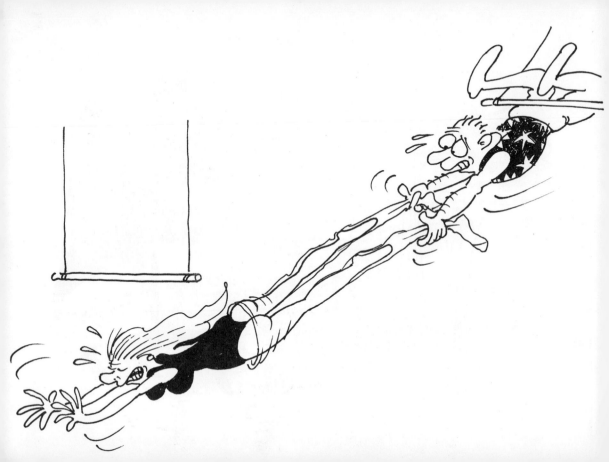

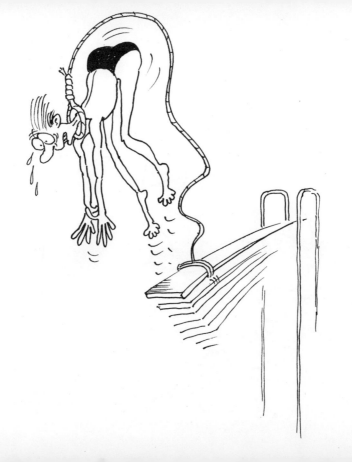

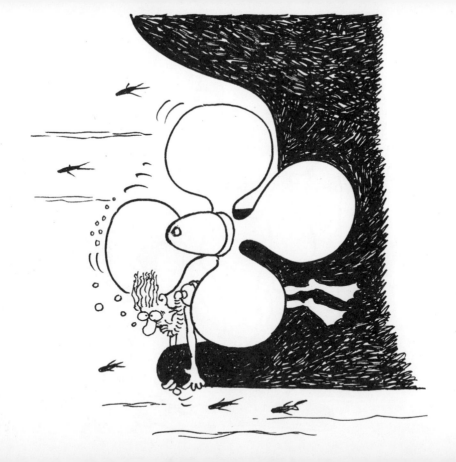

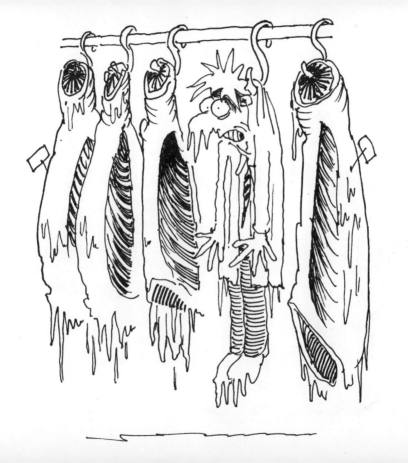

FOOD PAST ITS
SELL-BY DATE
↓

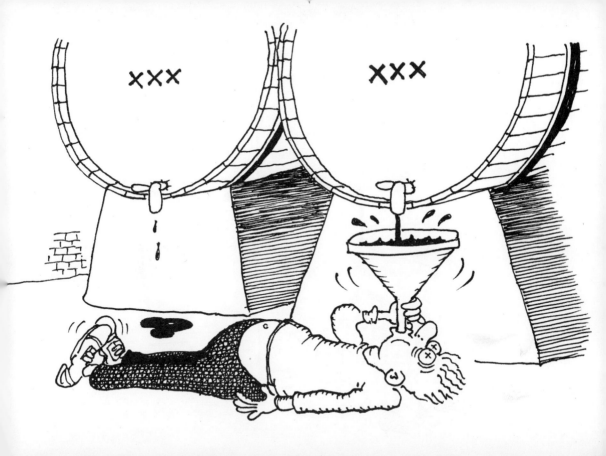

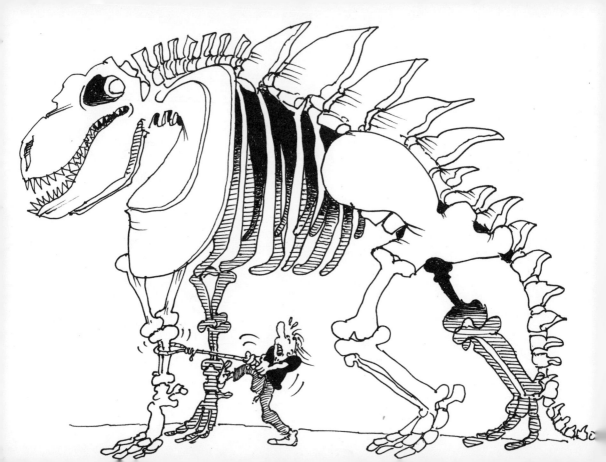

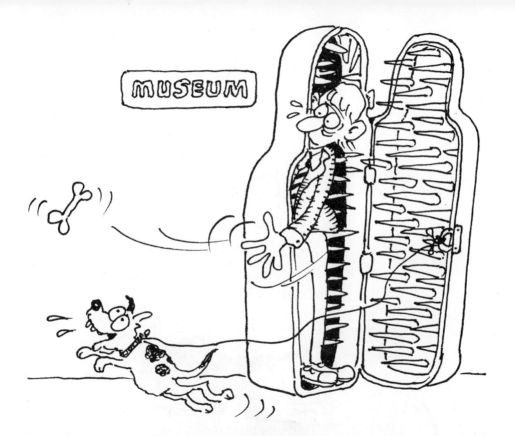

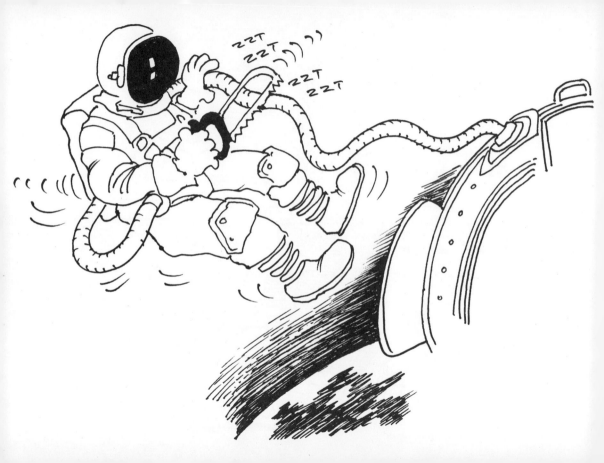

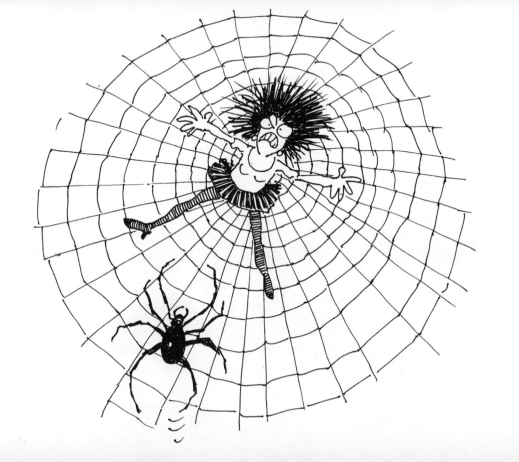

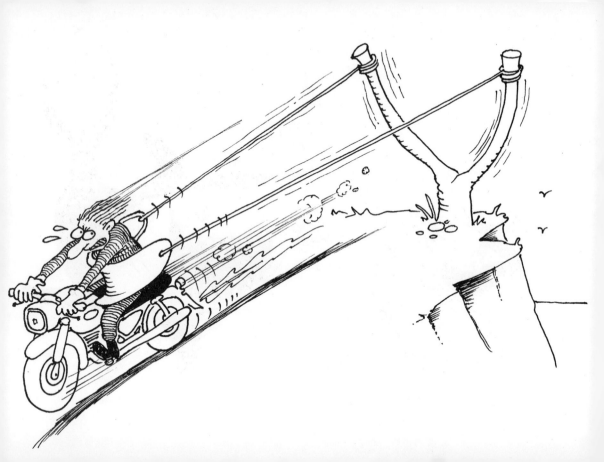

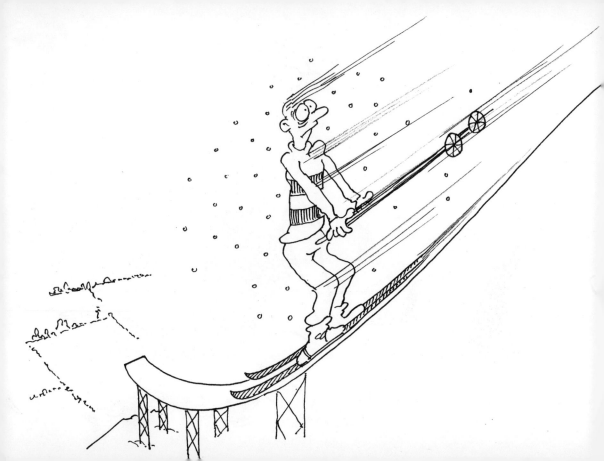